100% NEW

DEVELOPING LITERACY

Photocopiable teaching resources for literacy

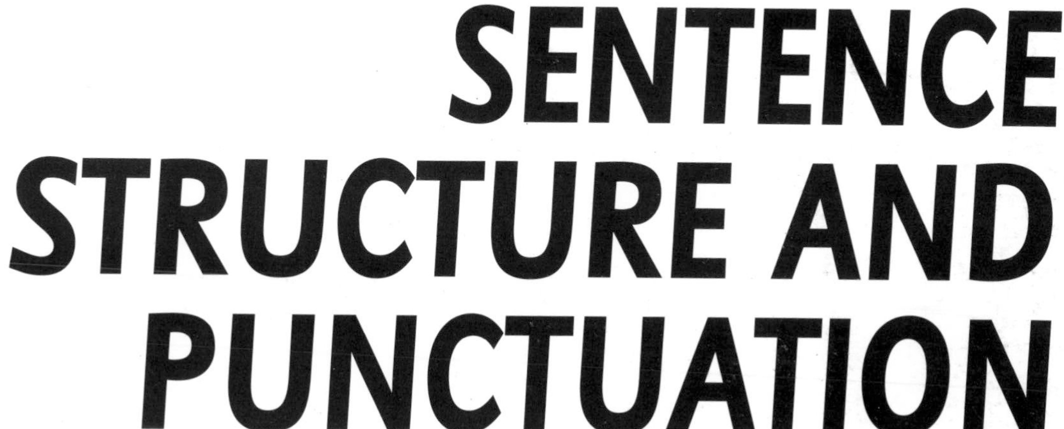

SENTENCE STRUCTURE AND PUNCTUATION

Ages 6–7

Christine Moorcroft

A & C Black • London

Contents

unctuation

struction and information sentences

etic sentences

blished 2007 by A & C Black Publishers Limited
Soho Square, London W1D 3HB
w.acblack.com

3N 978-0-7136-8455-1

tor: Dodi Beardshaw
signed by HL Studios, Oxford, and Susan MacIntyre

e author and publishers would like to thank Ray Barker and ur Lawrence for their advice in producing this series of books.

A CIP catalogue record for this book is available from the British Library.

Printed and bound in Great Britain by Martins the Printers, Berwick-on-Tweed.

A&C Black uses paper produced with elemental chlorine-free pulp, harvested from managed sustainable forests.

Introduction

100% New Developing Literacy: Sentence Structure and Punctuation is a series of seven photocopiable activity books for developing children's understanding of sentences and their ability to form sentences.

The books provide learning activities to support strand 11 (Sentence structure and punctuation) of the literacy objectives of the *Primary Framework for literacy and mathematics.*

The structure of **100% New Developing Literacy: Sentence Structure and Punctuation Ages 6–7** is designed to complement the structure of the Primary Framework for Ages 6–7, which focuses on the following types of text:

- narrative (stories with familiar settings, stories from a range of cultures, stories with predictable and patterned language, traditional and fairy tales, including plays, stories about fantasy settings)
- non-fiction (labels, lists and captions, instructions, recount, dictionary, information texts, recount – fact and fiction)
- poetry (using the senses, pattern and rhyme, poems on a theme).

100% New Developing Literacy: Sentence Structure and Punctuation Ages 6–7 addresses the following objectives from the Primary Framework:

- write simple and compound sentences;
- begin to use subordination in relation to time and reason;
- compose sentences using tense consistently (present and past);
- use question marks, and use commas to separate items in a list.

The sentence-level activities provided in this book support the children's reading and writing across different text-types, with a specific emphasis on those listed above: for example, the first section, **Story sentences** (pages 12–22), focuses mainly on sentences in the past tense (used in narrative writing), what characters did, where, when and why. The second section, **Sentence sense** (pages 23–32), supports this: it also provides a sound foundation for non-fiction writing. **All kinds of words** (pages 33–43) and **Punctuation** (pages 44–49) support both narrative and non-fiction writing. **Instruction and information sentences** (pages 50–58), supports non-fiction writing (instructions, explanations, information texts and non-chronological reports). The final section, **Poetic sentences** (pages 59–64), is linked to the language of poetry, making and recording observations and playing with language for fun.

Through the activities the children learn:

- what a sentence is;
- the difference between a word or group of words and a sentence;
- how to make a group of words into a sentence;
- how to turn notes into sentences;
- how to demarcate sentences with capital letters and full stops, question marks or exclamation marks;
- about using commas in lists and to separate parts c a sentence;
- about the present and past tenses and how to use ther consistently;
- about different types of word (for example, proper nouns an words for actions and describing, words for joining sentence and for saying how, when, where and why);
- about words which always start with a capital letters: fc example, I, names of people, places, titles, festivals, month and days;
- about the ways in which writers can help the reader know whic words are stressed: for example through italics and capitals.

Some of the activities can be carried out with the whole clas some are more suitable for small groups and others are fc individual work. Most of the activities require a written respons but some are presented in the form of games. They can be use for different purposes: to introduce skills needed for a particul type of writing, to support writing or to help with the assessme of children's progress.

Reading

Most children will be able to carry out the activitie independently. It is not expected that the children should be ab to read all the instructions on the sheets, but that someone w read them to or with them. Children gradually becor accustomed to seeing instructions, and learn their purpose lor before they can read them.

Organisation

The activities require very few resources besides penci crayons, scissors, glue and word-banks. Other materials a specified in the Teachers' notes at the bottom of each page: f example, information books and dictionaries.

Extension activities

Most of the activity sheets end with a challenge (**Now try this** which reinforces and extends the children's learning a provides the teacher with an opportunity for assessment. The more challenging activities might be appropriate for only a f children; it is not expected that the whole class should comple them. On some pages there is space for the children to comple the extension activities, but others will require a notebook o separate sheet of paper.

Accompanying CD-ROM

The enclosed CD-ROM contains electronic versions of the activity sheets in the book for printing, editing, savi or display on an interactive whiteboard. Our uniq browser-based interface makes it easy to select pag and to modify them to suit individual pupils' needs. S page 11 for further details.

Notes on the activities

ese notes for the teacher expand upon those which are ovided at the bottom of the activity pages. They give ideas and ggestions for making the most of the activity sheet, including ggestions for the whole-class introduction, the plenary session for follow-up work using an adapted version of the activity eet. To help teachers to select appropriate learning periences for their pupils, the activities are grouped into ctions within the book but the pages need not be presented in order in which they appear, unless stated otherwise.

tory sentences

he activities in this section mainly feature sentences in the ast tense. They support text-level work on narrative and rovide opportunities for the children to complete sentences, heck sentences for sense and use sentences as models for riting their own, including writing catchphrases for story haracters. You could make a display featuring a copied age from a story with parts of it labelled:

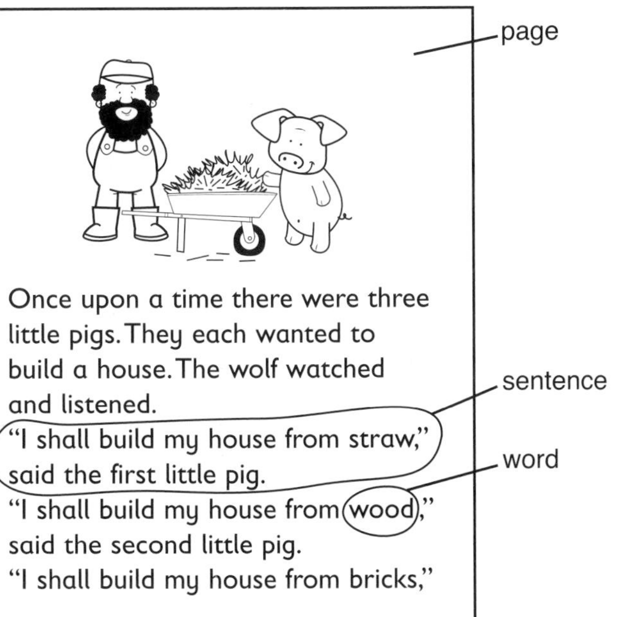

ntence snakes (page 12) reinforces the children's derstanding of a sentence and the difference between a ntence and a word and between a set of words or a line of xt and a sentence. You could also provide examples from ories and poems, read these with the children and discuss hether they are sentences and, if not, what needs to be done make them into sentences. This activity could be used to pport work in writing stories with familiar settings.

entence chart (page 13) reinforces the children's derstanding of a sentence and the difference between a ntence and a word, group of words or line of text. The ildren learn that a sentence says what happens and that it n say who or what did the action and what they did it to. They develop an understanding of the way in which sentences work. This activity could be used to support work in writing stories with familiar settings. During the plenary session volunteers could read out one of their sentences for the others to listen to and check.

Cross the road (page 14) helps the children to write simple sentences saying who did the action, what they did, and where. Those who undertake the extension activity could add a word or two to say when the action took place: for example, yesterday, this morning, this afternoon, last night, on Monday. Encourage each pair of children to share their completed page with another pair and to read one another's sentences aloud.

Sentence wall (page 15) develops skills in building longer sentences involving place and time. The children begin with a character who is the subject of the sentence and then a verb. They add words or phrases to say where or when the action took place. Encourage them to read the sentences aloud to check that they make sense. They could share their completed page with another pair of children who could check that they are sentences.

Sentence maker (page 16) develops skills in writing simple sentences without the support of a ready-planned format. The children are required to make a note of the words their counters land on and arrange these to form sentences, if they can. Some children might need adult help in order to recognise when they have collected enough words to make a sentence. You could ask them if they have a word for *who* and a word for *what they did*. Then ask them if they need anything else: for example, words for *where they did the action*.

Link up (page 17) provides sections of sentences saying who did the action, what they did and when. From these, the children create longer sentences. You could also play a game in which the class is split into three groups. Allocate to each group a question: *Who?*, *What did they do?* and *When?* At a given signal the children write an appropriate word on a card: the *Who?* group should write the name of a person or animal: for example, *Our teacher* (or the teacher's name), *My mum* or *I*. The *What did they do?* group should write an action: for example, climbed a tree, whistled a tune, sang a song, beat a drum. The *When?* group should write a word or group of words which say when the action happened: for example, *before breakfast*, *this morning*, *on Friday*. Invite a child from each group to come out and hold up his or her card, beginning with the *Who?* group, followed by *What did they do?* and then *When?* Invite a volunteer to read these aloud in the correct order. Draw out that this is a sentence.

But (page 18) introduces the connective word *but*. The children learn to link two simple sentences with *but* to form a compound sentence. You could also read out simple sentences and invite volunteers to add to them using *but*. Write up the sentences for the children to reread later.

Then (page 19) introduces the connective word *then*. The children learn to link two simple sentences with *then* to form a compound sentence. It is useful to point out that the name of the person doing the action is not usually repeated: for example, *She ate a cake and* (she) *drank some tea*, *We saw a flash of light and* (we) *heard a loud bang*. You could also read out simple sentences and invite volunteers to add to them using *then*. Write up the sentences for the children to reread later.

What for? and **Tell me why** (pages 20 and 21) requires the children to consider how to extend simple sentences to form complex sentences involving subordination by using the connectives *to* and *because* to indicate purpose. You could also read out simple sentences beginning with an action which can be followed by a purpose and invite volunteers to add to them using *to* or *because*, followed by an ending which says what the character did the action for. Write up the sentences for the children to reread later. It is useful to remind them that each sentence begins with a capital letter and ends with a full stop. Also remind them that a sentence can go past the end of a line.

Sentence link (page 22) reinforces the children's learning about how to join simple sentences to make compound sentences and complex sentences involving subordination. They are required to choose the most appropriate connective word. The children could also collect examples of sentences containing *and, but, then, because* or *to* from their reading.

Sentence sense

The activities in this section reinforce the children's previous learning about recognising a sentence and distinguishing between sentences and words and between sets of words and sentences. The children also identify what needs to be done to a set of words in order to make it into a sentence and construct compound sentences using subordination involving place, time and reason. This encourages proofreading and editing. The present and past tenses are introduced and the children learn how to form these and the need to use them consistently.

Find the sentences (page 23) helps the children to recognise sentences, including that sentences are not the same as lines o[f] text. They are asked to decide whether groups of words are sentences and to correct those which are not by adding appropriate words. Remind them that sentences say *who* did the action, *what* they did and, sometimes, *where, when* or *why*.

Sentence spinners (page 24) develops the children's understanding of how sentences work and how to construct longer sentences. It is useful to provide a sheet of paper on which the children can write the sentences they make. They could read these out during the plenary session. Encourage the[m] others to listen carefully and to say if they think they are not sentences, and why.

Silly sentences (page 25) develops the children's understanding of how sentences work. You will need to model how to write each segment of the sentence. The spinners from page 24 will help: for example *What did they do?* should be followed by a transitive verb (this term is not introduced to the children but can be demonstrated – *ate, bought, chased, caught, tickled, posted* and so on). The next section (*What did they do it to?*) requires a noun: for example, *an apple, a banana, a car, an elephant*). *Where?* requires a word or phrase for a place: for example, in the classroom, in town, at the shops in the playground. After the children have completed the strips by passing them around their groups invite them to open them up and read them aloud to the group.

Sentence robots (page 26) provides practice in writing simple sentences. You could add an extra challenge by timing this activity. Set an appropriate time target for the children (this could be varied within the class for children working at differen[t] levels). Some children could be asked to say what questions the sentence answer (*Who or what did it?, What did they do?* and *Where?*)

Word thief (page 27) develops the children's understanding of sentences by asking them to identify missing words. They nee[d] to consider the type of word which is missing. You could also set up a 'police investigation' in which you provide scraps of paper on which text has been printed but some words have been cut out. These could be 'secret messages' which the children as 'detectives' have to decipher.

Past change (page 28) introduces the past and present tense[s]. You could begin by demonstrating an action and asking the children what you are doing. Write up their responses as sentences in the second and first person: for example, *You are writing, I am writing, You are reading, I am reading*. Tell them about doing the same actions in the past: for example, *Yesterday I was writing, Yesterday I was reading*. Write these u[p] and ask the children which words have changed. Introduce th[e] shorter forms of these tenses: *I drive to school/I drove to scho[ol] You walk to school/You walked to school*. You could link this wi[th] word-level work on the ways in which words change accordin[g] to meaning.

day and yesterday (page 29) develops skills in using tenses. u could also provide quick practice by reading out a ntence which begins *Today* and asking the children to ange it so that it starts *Yesterday*. Remind them which other ord they should change.

ast mistakes (page 30) focuses on the correct forms and ellings of the past tense, including those of irregular verbs ch as *to eat*. This can be linked with word-level work on elling and suffixes. Draw out that most past tenses end with *d* and ask the children to spot any which do not. You could eate a class wall chart/word-bank of 'normal' past tenses to hich the children can contribute. Also challenge them to find ceptions and to write them on to a wall chart of exceptions. seful verbs to include are: run/ran, choose/chose, find/found, me/came, make/made, see/saw, hear/heard, feel/felt, ing/brought, send/sent, teach/taught, read/read, slide/slid, de/hid, draw/drew, drink/drank, swim/swam, fling/flung, atch/caught, say/said, ring/rang, fly/flew, grow/grew, row/threw, know/knew, and blow/blew.

ut it right (page 31) develops skills in using tenses onsistently. Remind the children of their previous work on nses and tell them that you are going to read out a passage hich has mistakes in it where the wrong tense is used. Ask em to listen carefully and to put up their hand when they hear mistake. Draw out that the day at the zoo happened in the ast and so the words for actions should show this. You could troduce the terms *verb* and *tense* if appropriate.

entence wizard (page 32) develops the children's nderstanding that a group of words has to be arranged in the orrect order to make sense as a sentence. Some children ight need to write the words on slips of paper so that they can hysically rearrange them. At the start of other lessons you ould reinforce the children's learning by speaking to them in ixed-up sentences and asking them what you should have aid. The children could also have opportunities for playing nixed-up speak' in which they talk to one another in mixed-up entences. Afterwards, ask them to write some of their mixed-up entences to check that they did not miss out any words. They an then rearrange the words in the correct order. Look for any xamples of a set of words which could be arranged in different rders to produce different sentences or even questions: for xample, *had a bike he* could be arranged to form *Had he a ike?* or *He had a bike.*

All kinds of words

This section is about the different types of word in a sentence. It focuses on similarities and differences between types of words. The terms for classes of words (for example, *noun*, *verb*) could be introduced if appropriate.

A pronoun substitutes for a noun: for example, *he* substitutes for *the man*, *the boy*, *William* and *so on*.

The personal pronouns are as follows:

	Singular personal pronouns		
Subject	I	you	he/she/it
Object	me	you	him/her/it

	Plural personal pronouns		
Subject	we	you	they
Object	us	you	them

Possessive pronouns denote ownership:

	Single possessive pronouns		
Subject	my	your	his/her/its
Object	mine	yours	his/hers/its

	Plural possessive pronouns		
Subject	our	your	their
Object	ours	yours	theirs

Prepositions show the relationship between a noun and the rest of a sentence. Examples include *after, along, at, before, beside, in*. They show how one part of a sentence is related to another in terms of time or space: for example, *They went to the shops after going swimming.*

Prepositions can consist of two or more words; these are referred to as complex prepositions: *near to, as far as, in front of.*

I, me and my (page 33) focuses on the personal pronouns *I*, *me* and *my* and the use of a capital *I*. You could begin by asking the children to listen to some sentences about you. Use your name throughout, without any personal pronouns, beginning with sentences requiring just one personal pronoun and building up to those requiring two and even three: for example, *Mrs Brown is talking to you, Mrs Brown put Mrs Brown's book on the table, Mrs Brown has Mrs Brown's pen, Give Mrs Brown Mrs Brown's pen, Mrs Brown would like you to give Mrs Brown Mrs Brown's pen.* You could also ask them to listen to sentences in which *I* and *me* are used incorrectly: for example, *Me would like you to listen, Listen to I.* After each sentence ask them if it sounds right for you to say it. Discuss why not and ask the children what you should say instead.

Instead of names (page 34) focuses on the personal pronouns *he, she, it* and *they*. You could reinforce the children's learning during the plenary session by saying the names of things or people and asking them for a word to use instead. Ask them how they know when to use *he, she, it* or *them*.

Belonging words (page 35) is about possessive pronouns. It develops the children's awareness of words to denote belonging. You could reinforce their learning during the plenary session by saying the names of things or people and asking them for a word to use for something belonging to them: for example, *Emma's coat, Jason's pencil, Anna and Raj's table, the cat's eye, the tree's trunk.* Ask them how they know when to use *his, her, its or their.* You could also ask what some of these owners themselves would say (*my coat, my pencil, our table*).

Where words (page 36) is about prepositions, although this term is not yet introduced to the children. These words help the children to compose compound sentences with subordination involving place. Remind them of the questions they have been asked when building sentences in their previous work: *Who (or what) did the action?, What did they do?, Where?, When?* and *Why?* The children could mime actions involving location or direction and the others could identify the *Where* words and then compose sentences to say what they are doing: for example, *Kit is crawling along the mat, Mair is hopping across the floor.*

Tell me when (page 37) is about words indicating time. Remind the children of the questions they have been asked when building sentences in their previous work: *Who (or what) did the action?, What did they do?, Where?, When?* and *Why?* You could also show the children the class timetable and help them to compose sentences about when specific activities are carried out.

It's like this (page 38) is about adjectives, although this term is not introduced to the children. It develops the children's understanding that there are different types of words and that they are used for different purposes in sentences. This page could be linked with work in science on materials. The children could contribute to a wall display of pictures of objects and materials by writing captions consisting of simple sentences to describe them.

Words for doing (page 39) is about verbs. This term is not used, although teachers might wish to introduce it to some children if appropriate. It develops the children's understanding that there are different types of words and that they are used for different purposes in sentences. This page could be linked with work in science on materials. The children could contribute to a wall display of pictures of objects and materials by writing captions consisting of simple sentences to describe them.

Answer to word search:

g	r	o	w	s	o	n	i	r	e	a	d
y	z	w	a	s	h	o	h	d	p	i	r
b	c	r	o	q	o	s	k	a	t	e	i
p	n	i	a	r	p	w	n	d	o	w	n
c	a	t	k	n	d	i	i	u	a	s	k
q	l	e	j	x	c	m	t	o	p	e	o

Question words (page 40) is about words which introduce questions: *how, what, when, where, who* and *why*. It develops the children's understanding that there are different types of words and that they are used for different purposes in sentences. The children could also identify questions which begin with these words in books they read and copy some of these in coloured writing onto strips of paper to display on a questions board. Remind them that questions always end with a question mark.

Special names (page 41) consolidates the children's learning about proper nouns. You could introduce the terms *noun* for words that name things and *proper noun* for names which begin with capital letters. Remind them that place names begin with capital letters, as do days, months and the names of festivals. This could be linked with work in RE on festivals and their dates. Encourage the children to notice other words in texts they read which begin with a capital letter: for example, brand names. Draw out that words such as *boy, girl, day, month* and *festival* do not have a capital letter but words for one of these do: *Harry, Abby, Monday, December, Divali.*

Addresses (page 42) consolidates the children's learning about proper nouns. You could use the terms *noun* for words that name things and *proper noun* for names which begin with capital letters. Remind them that place names begin with capital letters and invite them to help you to write the name and address of the school. Which words do they think should begin with a capital letter? This could be linked with work in geography on the difference between roads, towns, cities, countries and so on.

Book titles (page 43) consolidates the children's learning about proper nouns. You could use the terms *noun* for words that name things and *proper noun* for names which begin with capital letters. Encourage them to use a capital letter for the main words in the titles of stories they write.

unctuation

ıese activities consolidate the children's understanding of the ɜe of a capital letter and a full stop to demarcate the ɘginning and end of a sentence and a question mark to end question. Other punctuation marks are introduced: ‹clamation marks and commas.

ying sentences (page 44) consolidates the children's ability use capital letters and full stops to demarcate sentences.

ıestion mark and **Question queen** (pages 45 and 46) are ›out sentences which are questions. The children learn how to 'm a question mark and how to position it on a line of writing. s useful to ask the children some questions and for them to swer them and then let the children ask some questions for ıers to answer. Draw out which sentences need full stops and ıich need question marks. You could point out that part of a estion mark is the same as a full stop because it belongs at ɘ end of a sentence. The part above the full stop shows that ɘ sentence is a question. The children could take turns to ake up their own 'I want…' sentences in which they describe ɘ items they list.

nail check (page 47) is about distinguishing between ıestions and other sentences. It is useful to ask the children me questions and for them to answer them and then let the ıildren ask some questions for others to answer. Draw out ıich sentences need full stops and which need question arks. You could point out that part of a question mark is the me as a full stop because it belongs at the end of a ntence. The part above the full stop shows that the sentence a question. The children could take turns to make up their vn 'I want…' sentences in which they describe the items they t. You could also provide opportunities for them to identify the ›propriate punctuation keys on a keyboard.

ıestion time (page 48) focuses on changing a sentence into question. In addition to exchanging the full stop for a question ark, the children learn how to alter the order of the words to ake a sentence into a question.

ıe comma (page 49) shows the children how to form a ›mma. You could demonstrate how it is used by reading a list thout a pause between each item. Read the completed ample with the children and encourage them to follow the text th a finger and pause at each comma as you pause slightly ıring the reading.

Instruction and information sentences

This section is about sentences in the imperative (command) form – although this term is not yet introduced – and sentences which give information. Also included are writing notes and using diagrams, keys and charts. The activities support the writing of non-fiction.

What do you know? (page 50) is about reading questions and answering them by writing sentences which give information. It can be used to support work in various subjects in which the children are asked to find out about a topic from information books, the Internet and electronic texts.

Instruction search (page 51) helps the children to recognise the style of a sentence which is an instruction. Draw out how these are different from information sentences by focusing on how they begin and on the form of the verb.

Recipe sentences (page 52) focuses on writing instructions. It develops the children's awareness of the style of sentence used in instructions. They could discuss the pictures with a partner and then collaborate on the instruction they give. They could also write one-sentence instructions for use at school. They might find it easier to begin sentences: 'You…'. Remind them to start with a capital letter and end with a full stop.

Note it and **Notes to sentences** (pages 53 and 54) focus on writing notes and composing sentences based on notes. The children learn what is meant by writing notes – writing only the important words. It helps them to find information and then write it in their own words. This could be linked with work in geography.

Island key and **Reading a chart** (pages 55 and 56) develop skills in interpreting keys and using charts and writing sentences which communicate information from them. These could be linked with work in geography.

Chart it (page 57) encourages the children to read sentences and record the information from them on a chart. Draw out that this is a useful way of making notes. It could be used in connection with work in science or geography.

It's magnetic (page 58) develops skills in interpreting diagrams and composing sentences to communicate information from diagrams. It could be linked with work in science or geography. Children could use the Internet or information books when doing the extension activity.

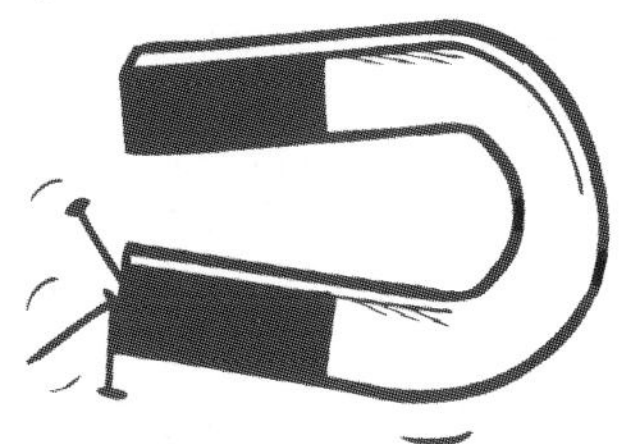

Poetic sentences

The activities in this section feature sentences from poems. Tell the children that poems need not be written in sentences but that many of them are and that poets explore interesting ways of putting words together. In these activities the focus is on developing the children's understanding of what is meant by a sentence and their ability to recognise that a sentence can say something silly yet still make sense as a sentence. There are also activities about how to show a stress or emphasis on words by using italics or capital letters. These activities provide opportunities for links with ICT.

Patterns in poems (page 59) develops the children's appreciation that poems can be written in sentences but that some are not. They identify the lines of poetry which make up a sentence and those which do not.

Fun change and **That's a laugh** (pages 60 and 61) are about making small changes to sentences to create humour. The children learn that a sentence can make sense as a sentence even if it says something silly.

***Loud* words** and **LOUD words** (pages 62 and 63) help the children to recognise how the style of text helps to communica feelings or helps the reader to read a sentence with expressio It is useful to provide opportunities for the children to convert a word to italics by highlighting a word (or just placing the curso between any two letters of a word) and then using the Italic ico or Control and I. Some children might be able to change a wo from lower- to upper-case by highlighting it or placing the curs between any two letters, selecting Change case from the Format menu tab and then selecting upper case.

That's silly (page 64) helps the children to write humorous sentences by providing beginnings and endings they can match up. This activity encourages them to think about the way in which the sentence makes sense as they are required to think about the grammatical match of beginning to ending: for example *Two old octopuses* could not be followed by *and brushed.*

Using the CD-ROM

ıe PC CD-ROM included with this book contains an ısy-to-use software program that allows you to print out ıges from the book, to view them (e.g. on an interactive ıiteboard) or to customise the activities to suit the ıeds of your pupils.

etting started

s easy to run the software. Simply insert the CD-ROM to your CD drive and the disk should autorun and unch the interface in your web browser.

the disk does not autorun, open 'My Computer' and ılect the CD drive, then open the file 'start.html'.

ease note: this CD-ROM is designed for use on a PC. It ll also run on most Apple Macintosh computers in ıfari however, due to the differences between Mac and C fonts, you may experience some unavoidable ıriations in the typography and page layouts of the ctivity sheets.

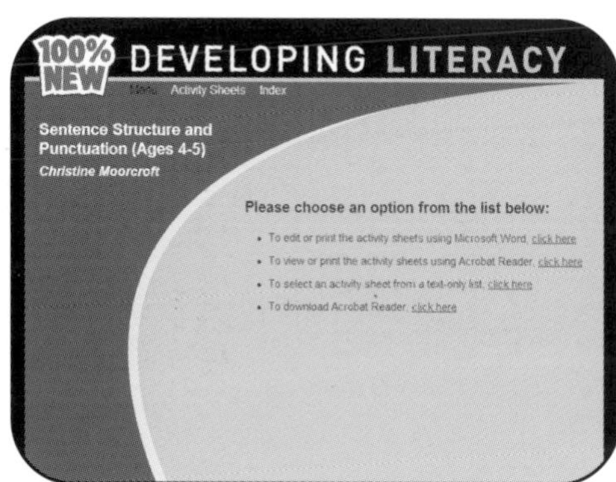

he Menu screen

ıur options are available to you from the main menu ıreen.

ıe first option takes you to the Activity Sheets screen, ıere you can choose an activity sheet to edit or print out ıing Microsoft Word.

you do not have the Microsoft Office suite, you might e to consider using OpenOffice instead. This is a multi-atform and multi-lingual office suite, and an 'open-ource' project. It is compatible with all other major office ıites, and the product is free to download, use and stribute. The homepage for OpenOffice on the Internet www.openoffice.org.)

ıe second option on the main menu screen opens a ⊃F file of the entire book using Adobe Reader (see ılow). This format is ideal for printing out copies of the ctivity sheets or for displaying them, for example on an teractive whiteboard.

ıe third option allows you to choose a page to edit from text-only list of the activity sheets, as an alternative to e graphical interface on the Activity Sheets screen.

Adobe Reader is free to download and to use. If it is not already installed on your computer, the fourth link takes you to the download page on the Adobe website.

You can also navigate directly to any of the three screens at any time by using the tabs at the top.

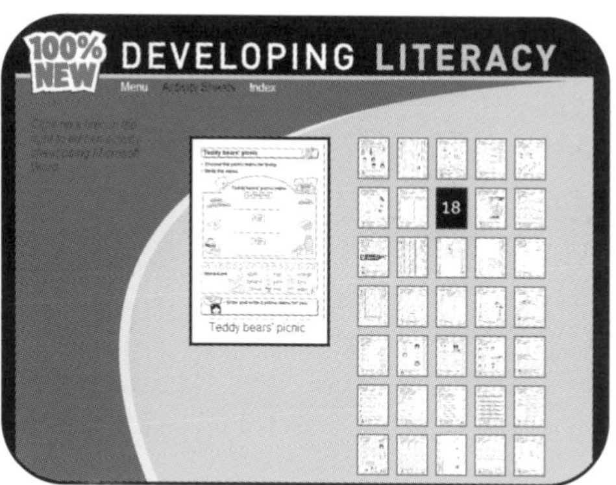

The Activity Sheets screen

This screen shows thumbnails of all the activity sheets in the book. Rolling the mouse over a thumbnail highlights the page number and also brings up a preview image of the page.

Click on the thumbnail to open a version of the page in Microsoft Word (or an equivalent software program, see above.) The full range of editing tools are available to you here to customise the page to suit the needs of your particular pupils. You can print out copies of the page or save a copy of your edited version onto your computer.

The Index screen

This is a text-only version of the Activity Sheets screen described above. Choose an activity sheet and click on the 'download' link to open a version of the page in Microsoft Word to edit or print out.

Technical support

If you have any questions regarding the *100% New Developing Literacy* or *Developing Mathematics* software, please email us at the address below. We will get back to you as quickly as possible.

educationalsales@acblack.com

Sentence snakes

- **Colour the snakes which have sentences.**
- **Make the others into sentences.**
- **Write them on the blank snakes.**

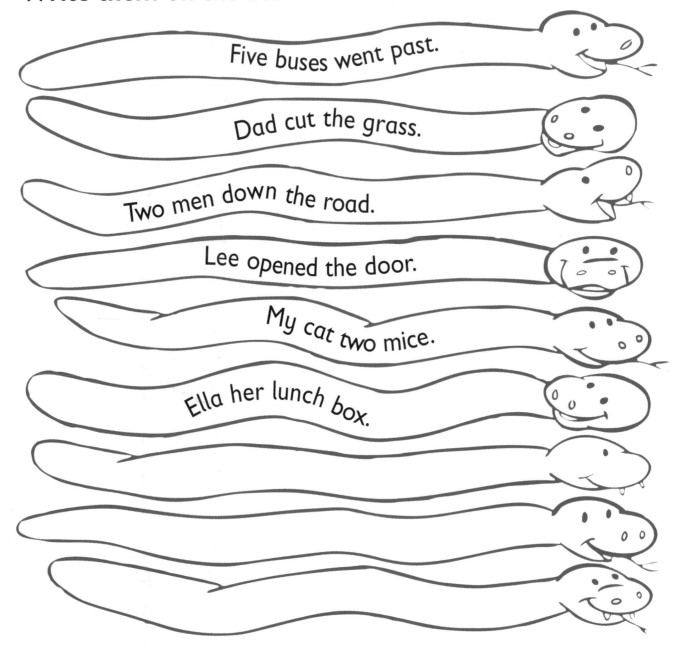

Five buses went past.

Dad cut the grass.

Two men down the road.

Lee opened the door.

My cat two mice.

Ella her lunch box.

NOW TRY THIS!

- **Write sentences about these.**

a car a banana a bee

Teachers' note Read the words on the first snake with the children. Ask them if they make sense. Draw out that these words tell them something and make sense. They are a sentence. You could also ask the children to count the words in the sentence in order to reinforce their understanding of the meanings of *word* and *sentence*. Provide crayons for colouring so that the words can still be read.

Sentence chart

Look at the pictures.
Think about...

Write sentences on the chart.

	Who?	What?	
Dad	Dad	posted	a letter.
Rosie		kicked	
Mum			
Jason			
Tim			
Holly			

Word-bank

dropped licked a ball a cup
found picked a flower a lollipop a pound

NOW TRY THIS!

• **Write a sentence about each picture.**

Teachers' note Write up some words which are connected in some way but do not form a sentence, such as the third example on page 12. Draw out why it is not a sentence (there is no word to say what the two men were doing or to link *two men* with *down the road*). Read the completed example on this page and ask who or what the sentence is about (Dad) and what he did.

Cross the road

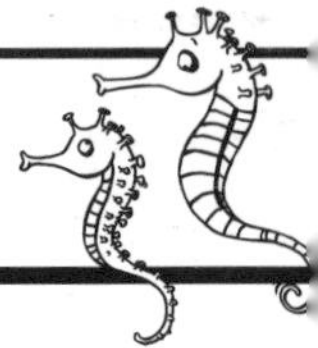

- **Play with a partner.**
- **Take turns to colour a footprint to make a sentence.**
- **Join these footprints. The first to cross the road wins.**

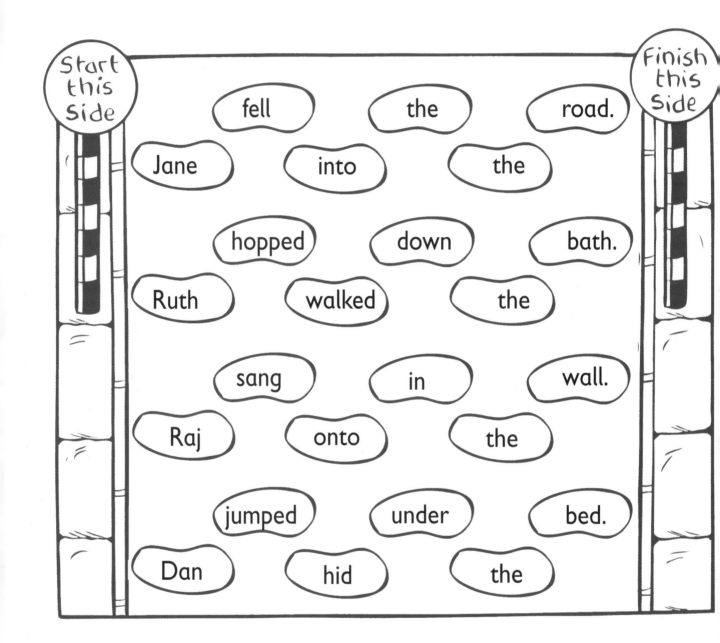

Start this side

fell the road.

Jane into the

hopped down bath.

Ruth walked the

sang in wall.

Raj onto the

jumped under bed.

Dan hid the

Finish this side

- **Copy two of your sentences.**
- **Add one or two words to make them longer.**

Teachers' note Model how to complete a sentence: start with the person the sentence is about (for example, Jane) and then choose a word for what she did. Ask what could come next. It is useful to think aloud and explain why **fell** or **hopped** cannot come next, using *the* + *road* or *the* + *bath* as examples: Jane could not fall or hop anything but she could fall *into* the bath or *down* the road.

Sentence wall

- **Play with a partner. Take turns to colour a brick. The first to cross the wall with a sentence wins.**

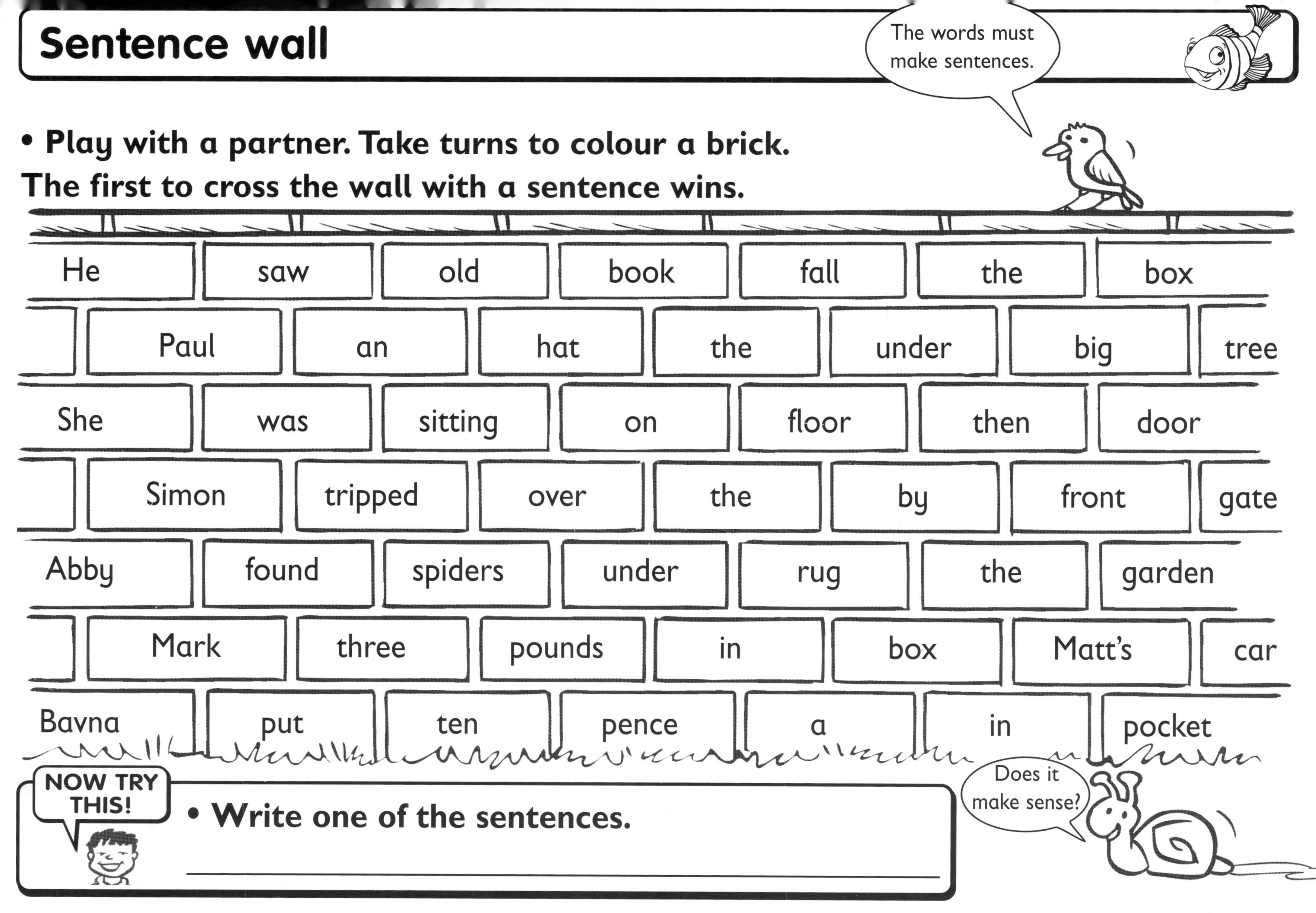

NOW TRY THIS!

- **Write one of the sentences.**

achers' note Remind the children of the difference between a list of words and a sentence. Draw out at a sentence has to make sense and to tell the reader something. Explain that the bricks must touch e another but they can be on different rows and demonstrate how to complete a sentence. Remind e children that it starts with the person or thing it is about: for example, *He, Paul, She.*

Sentence maker

- **Roll the dice.**
- **Move your counter.**
- **Write the words you land on.**

Can you make a sentence?

You need:

dice · paper · shaker · pencil

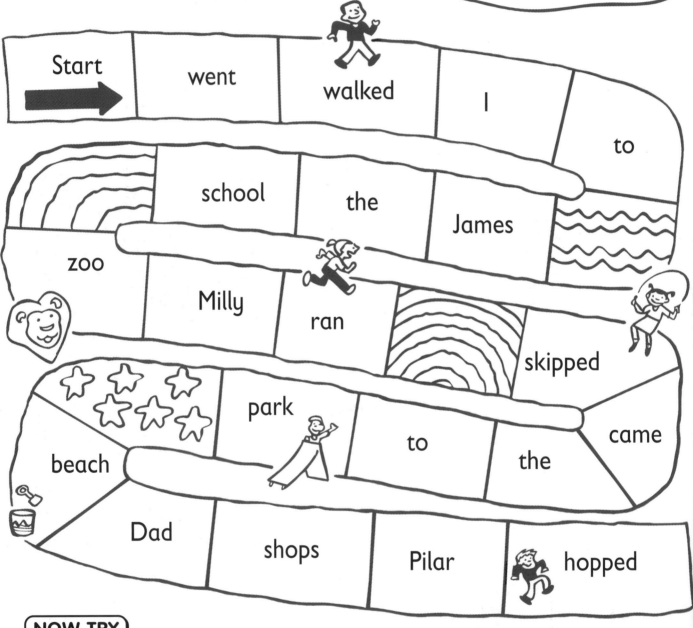

Start → went · walked · I · to · James · the · school · zoo · Milly · ran · skipped · came · the · to · park · beach · Dad · shops · Pilar · hopped

- **Use the words on the game board to write two sentences.**

Teachers' note Ask children to work in groups of four. Provide pencils or pens and small pieces of paper for them all to record the words they land on. Encourage them to read the words they have written after each throw and make a sentence with them. After the next throw they could add a word to an existing sentence, begin a new one or move a word from one sentence to another.

Link up

Join three large owls to make sentences.

Who?

two boys | an old woman | ten girls | Mr Jones | my mum

What?

got lost | went to town | lost a hat | sang a song | slid down the slide

When?

last night. | at bedtime. | after tea. | this morning. | yesterday.

NOW TRY THIS!

- **Write three other sentences which answer these questions.**

Who? What? When?

achers' note Point out that the owls should be linked down, not across, the page. Draw tention to the questions *Who?, What*? and *When?* Draw out that each sentence begins with the rson or thing it is about. Next come some words to say *what* he, she or it did (and sometimes here). Finally come some words to say *when* it happened. Model an example.

But

- **Read the sentences.**
- **Join each sentences to an ending.**
- **Write but on the line.**
- **Read the long sentences.**

	but	
I like apples and bananas	but	it starts first time every day.
Ella can run fast		he came last in the high jump.
Jay won the long jump		I don't like grapes.
This soup is too hot		Mum likes France better.
My Dad wants to go to Spain		she can't swim.
Our car is very old		that one is too cold.

NOW TRY THIS!

- **Make these sentences longer.**

I like playing football

Dan's house is very big

Amy has a big brown dog

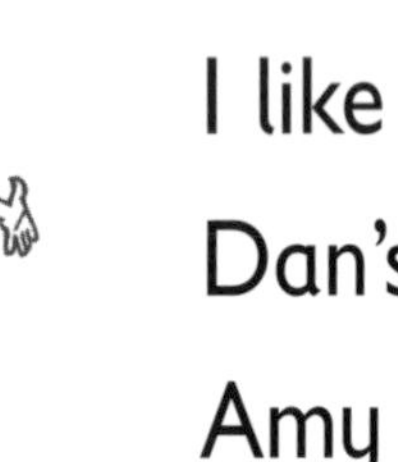

Teachers' note Explain that we can join two sentences to make one long sentences: one way of doing this is to put in a word which makes sense, such as *and* or *but*. Remind the children how *and* is used: *I came home and I played with Ella*. Point out that sentences can be joined with *but* if you want to show a difference. Read the completed example with them and discuss why *but* is used.

Then

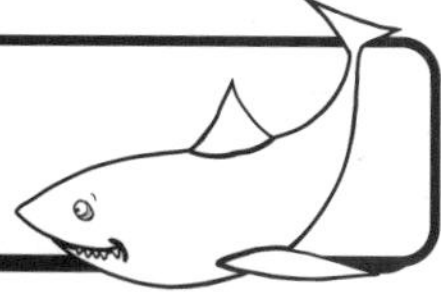

Read the sentence starts.
Join each start to an ending.
Draw a line.
Write then **on the line.**
Read the long sentence.

She ate a cake	it began to rain.
We saw a flash of light	went out for a walk.
He put on his coat	a man got out.
A big black cloud came	heard a loud bang.
The car stopped	drank some tea.

then

NOW TRY THIS!

- **Make these sentences longer.**

He put a stamp on the letter

I came home from school

…chers' note Remind the children of the words they know for joining sentences (*and* and *but*). …ad the example and point out why *then* is useful for joining these sentences: it shows that one …ng happens *after* the other. Discuss: *I came home and I played with Ella*. Draw out that *then* …uld be used instead of *and*. This would stress that one thing happened *after* the other.

What for?

- **Read the sentence starts.**
- **Choose an ending.**
- **Write [to], then the ending.**
- **Read the longer sentence.**

Jack and Jill went up the hill [to] fetch a pail of water.

Old Mother Hubbard went  ______________________

She went to the baker's [ ] ______________________

Here is a candle [ ] 

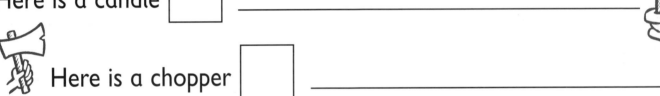

Here is a chopper 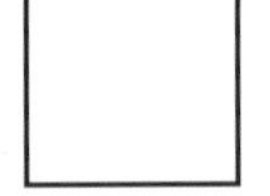 ______________________

Endings

chop off your head.	to buy him some bread.
to light you to bed.	to the cupboard.

- **Write new endings for these sentences.**

I ran down the road.

I turned on the tap.

Teachers' note Revise the words the children know for joining sentences (*and*, *but* and *then*). Draw out in the example that Jack and Jill did two things. Ask for two sentences about these actions. Point out why *to* is useful for joining them: to show *why* Jack and Jill went up the hill. Also point out that another change had to be made and ask the children if they can spot it (*fetched* is changed to *fetch*).

Tell me why

Finish the sentences.

Use because.

She put on her coat because ______________________________

____.

Saqib ran to school [   ] ______________________

____.

My sister cried [   ] ______________________

____.

Dad told us off [   ] ______________________

____.

I had a cake with candles [   ] ______________

____.

Mum told us to come indoors [   ] ____________

____.

- **Answer the question. Write a sentence.**

  Why did the gingerbread man run away?

Teachers' note Remind the children of how they joined sentences in a way which showed why something was done (using *to*). Read the first example and ask them what they could write after *because*: for example, *it was cold*. Draw out that two sentences are joined to show *why*.

Sentence link

- **Make long sentences.**
- **Write** and, but, then, because **or** to.

1 We went to town [ ] buy some shoes.

2 He bent down [ ] picked up a coin.

3 She can sing [ ] she can't dance.

4 We couldn't play football [ ] the pitch was flooded.

5 They ran to the corner [ ] looked for Milly.

6 Rosie could see the moon [ ] she couldn't see any stars

7 The little boy cried [ ] he was lost.

8 Mum gave me some money [ ] buy a book.

NOW TRY THIS!

- **Write five long sentences.**
- **Use these words in them.**

and but then because to

Teachers' note Remind the children of the words they know for joining sentences (*and, but, then, because* and *to*). Read the example and ask the children to try different words in the gap. Discuss which is best, and why. They could then read the sentences with a friend and discuss which word would make the best sense in each gap.

Find the sentences

Are these sentences? ✓ or ✗

Tell a friend how you know.

An old black car was parked outside. ☐

He under the bushes and jumped over the wall. ☐

There once an old woman who lived in a cave. ☐

Gran was in bed because she was ill. ☐

We saw a bright light in the pine woods. ☐

The school very big with over eighty children. ☐

- **Look again at the flags which are not sentences.**
- **Make them into sentences.**

____

____

____

____

- **Copy a long sentence from a book.**
- **Miss out a word.**
- **Is it still a sentence?**

Teachers' note Use this to review the children's understanding of what a sentence is. In addition to checking which sets of words are sentences, the children could circle the person or thing the sentence is about in red and what he, she or it did in blue. They could then read the rest of the sentence and decide what this tells them: for example, *where, when* or *why*.

Sentence spinners

Who?

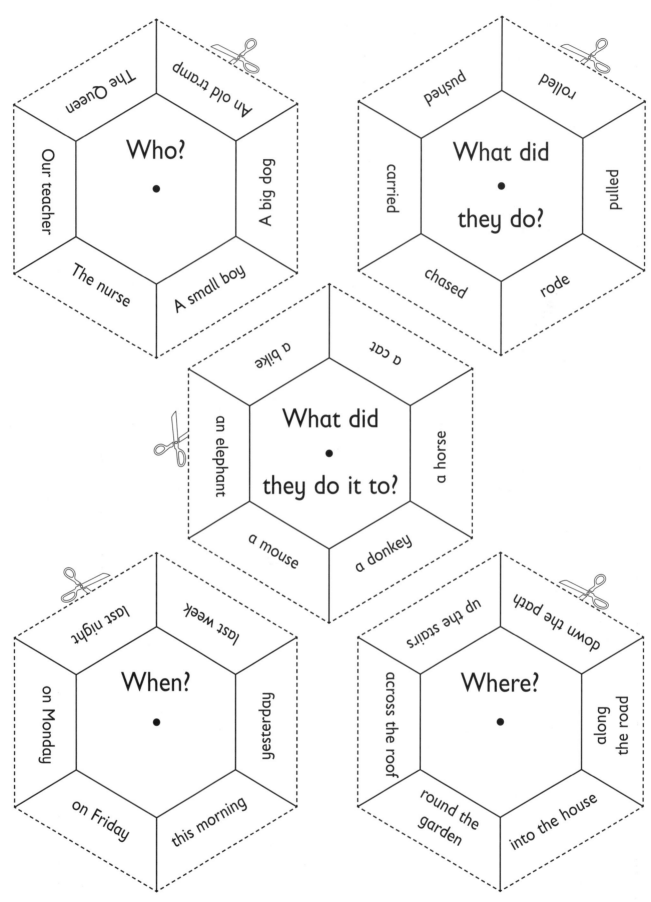

- The Queen
- An old tramp
- A big dog
- A small boy
- The nurse
- Our teacher

What did they do?

- pushed
- rolled
- pulled
- rode
- chased
- carried

What did they do it to?

- a bike
- a cat
- a horse
- a donkey
- a mouse
- an elephant

When?

- last night
- last week
- yesterday
- this morning
- on Friday
- on Monday

Where?

- up the stairs
- down the path
- along the road
- into the house
- round the garden
- across the roof

Teachers' note Remind the children of their previous work on sentence-building and read the questions on the four outer spinners. Read the question on the middle spinner and discuss which actions can be done to each thing. Copy the page on to card and cut out the spinners. Push a matchstick or cocktail stick through the centre. You could number the spinners to show in which order to use them.

Silly sentences

Who?	Who?	Who?	Who?
The clown	Mr Grim	Mrs Smiley	The police officer
What did they do?	What did they do?	What did they do?	What did they do?
What did they do it to?	What did they do it to?	What did they do it to?	What did they do it to?
Where?	Where?	Where?	Where?

[Te]achers' note Cut out the vertical strips and give one to each child. Fold under the top solid line so [th]at the children cannot see the character. They write what a character did and to what or to whom, [th]en fold the strip under at the next dotted line to hide this, before passing it to another member of [th]e group who writes where the action was done. Then they open the strips and read the sentences.

Sentence robots

Help the robots to make sentences.
- **Circle a set of words from each robot.**
- **Write the sentences.**

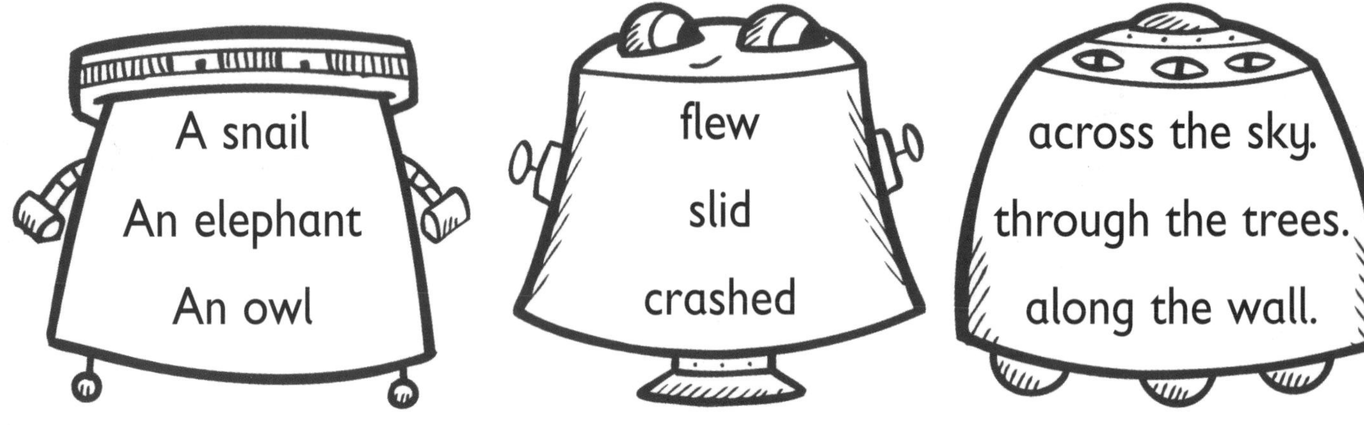

The train
The car
The bike
sped
rattled
chugged
under the bridge.
along the track.
down the lane.

- **Make three sentences from the robots' words.**
- **Add another word to make longer sentences.**

Teachers' note Tell the children that they are going to choose a word or set of words from each robot to make a sentence reading across the page. They could make this either silly or sensible. Ask them questions about the sentence: *Who? What did it do? Where?*

Word thief

he word thief has struck.
Put the words back in the gaps.

and	in	on	bread	make
it	out	put	eat	toaster

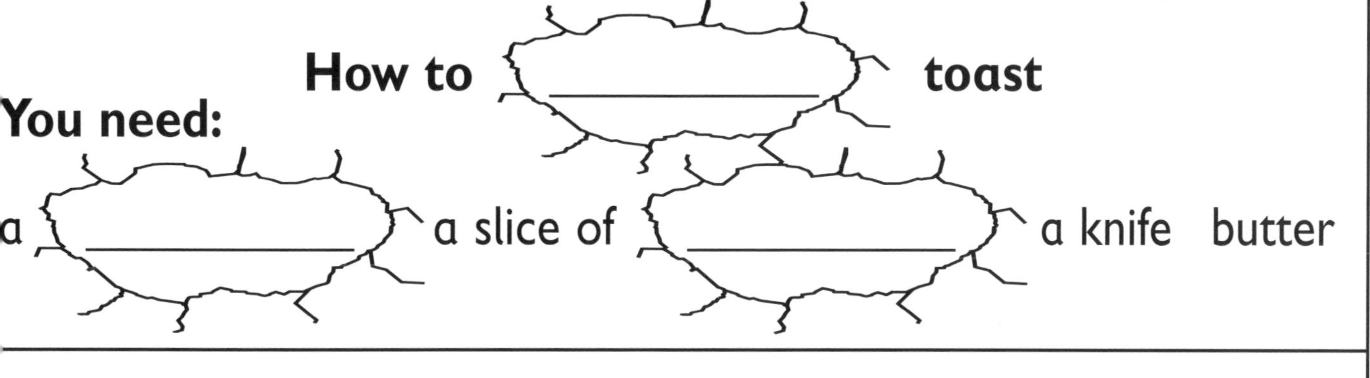

How to ______ toast

You need:

a ______ a slice of ______ a knife butter

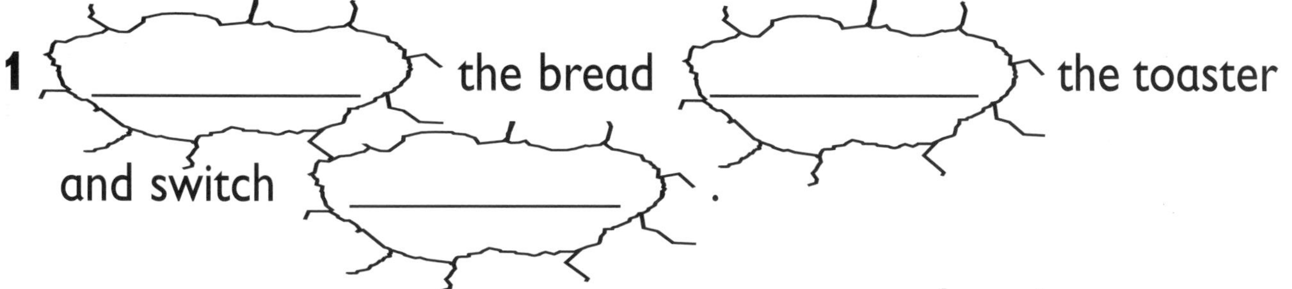

1 ______ the bread ______ the toaster and switch ______.

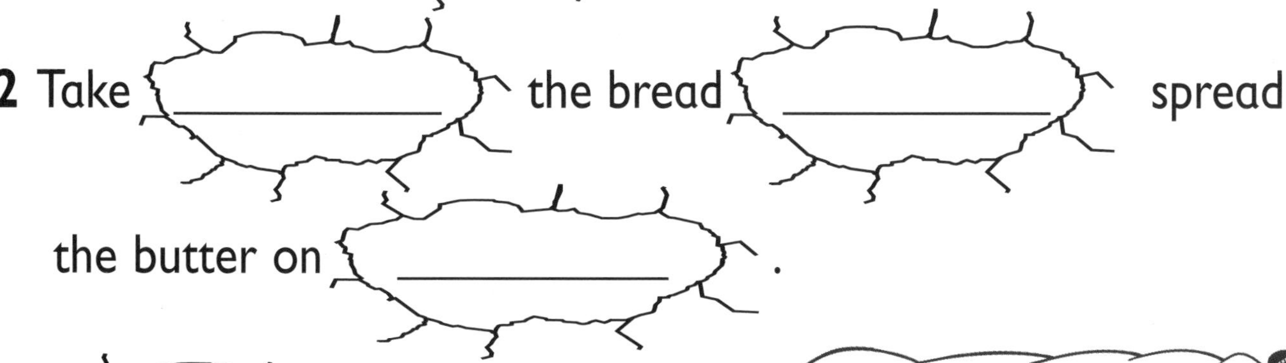

2 Take ______ the bread ______ spread the butter on ______.

3 ______ the toast.

- **Write three sentences.**
- **Miss out two words in each.**
- **Ask a friend what is missing.**

achers' note Tell the children that they are going to read instructions for making toast but at the word thief has stolen some of the words. Their task is to put the words back where ey belong.

Past change

Now	Then
I am talking or I talk	I was talking or I talked

- **Fill in the gaps.**

Now	Then
I am walking. I walk.	I was ________. I ________.
I am ________. I ________.	I was ________. I sang.
I am ________. I ________.	I was sitting. I ________.
I am playing. I ________.	I was ________. I ________.
I am ________. I eat.	I was ________. I ate.

NOW TRY THIS!

- **Write** now **and** then **sentences using these words:**

jump ride

Teachers' note Explain that we change the words for what we do depending on whether we are doing it now or have already done it. Demonstrate how to complete the first question and give examples of sentences in which the verbs are used: for example, *I am walking to school now, I walk to school every day, I was walking to school when I met my friend, I walked to school this morning.*

Today and yesterday

Today | I am going | to school.

Yesterday | I went | to school.

Fill in the gaps.

Today I am playing football.

Yesterday ______________________ .

Today I am walking to school.

Yesterday ______________________ .

Today I am having a school dinner.

Yesterday ______________________ .

Today I am doing maths.

Yesterday ______________________ .

Today I am writing a story.

Yesterday ______________________ .

NOW TRY THIS!

- **Write sentences for today using these.**

  eating | singing | watching

- **Change the sentences to yesterday.**

Teachers' note Remind the children that we change the words for what we do depending on whether we are doing it now or have already done it. Read the completed example and demonstrate how to complete the first one. The children could give other examples of their own. You could link this with word-level work on the ways in which words change according to meaning.

Past mistakes

This is right **.**

Today I wait

Yesterday I waited

This is wrong ✗**.**

Today I eat

Yesterday I eated

Are these right or wrong? ✔ **or** ✗

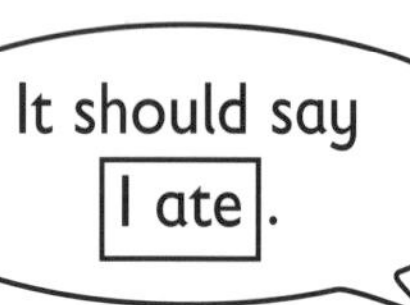

Today I skip.
Yesterday I skipped. ☐

Today I speak.
Yesterday I speaked. ☐

Today I write.
Yesterday I writed. ☐

Today I sing.
Yesterday I singed. ☐

Today I dance.
Yesterday I danced. ☐

Today I go.
Yesterday I goed. ☐

NOW TRY THIS!

- **Copy the wrong words.**
- **Write them correctly.**

________ ✗ ________ ✗ ________ ✗ ________ ✗

________ ✔ ________ ✔ ________ ✔ ________ ✔

Teachers' note Remind the children of their previous learning about the changes we make to 'doing' words depending on whether we are doing it now or have already done it. Introduce the terms *past* and *present*. Read the completed example to the children before giving them a copy of the page. Ask them which examples are correct and what is wrong with *I eated*.

Put it right

- **The words in boxes are wrong.**
- **Write the correct words.**

Our day at the zoo

First we went to see the monkeys.

They [are playing] ________________ on ropes.

We [watch] ______________ them for a while. Then we went to

the elephant house. An elephant [squirts] ____________ water

everywhere. It [is] _______ fun. Our teacher got soaked.

A tiger [growls] ______________ and scared us, but the lions

[take] __________ no notice of us. It started to

rain just as we got into the bus to come back.

NOW TRY THIS!

- **Write three sentences about your favourite day out.**

Teachers' note Remind the children of the meanings of past and present. Tell them that they are going to read a recount about a day at the zoo. Stress that it happened in the past but that the writer made some mistakes, sometimes writing as if it were happening now (in the present). Tell them that their task is to correct these words.

Sentence wizard

- **The wizard has cast a spell on the sentences.**
- **Write them correctly.**

1 waved I wand. my magic

2 mixed I words. the up

3 spells. know I magic a lot of

4 spell. my best This is very

5 broom. Need a wand and Wizards a

6 fly on and Wizards their brooms wave wands. their

1 ______________________________

2 ______________________________

3 ______________________________

4 ______________________________

5 ______________________________

6 ______________________________

NOW TRY THIS!

- **Write two sentences.**
- **Write them again with the words mixed up.**
- **Give them to a friend to write correctly.**

Teachers' note Remind the children that a set of words can make sense as a sentence only if they are in the correct order. Ask them to read the first example and to say whether it is a sentence. Does it make sense? Ask them to change the order of the words. They could try this on the board or on scrap paper.

I, me and my

Use I **or** me **instead of your name.**

I went to the fair.

Mum came with me.

This is my mum.

Use my **for things that belong to you.**

Write I **,** me **or** my **in the gaps.**

____ would like an apple.

That is ____ apple.

Please give ____ an apple.

Sam gave ____ a sweet.

____ gave Sam a sweet.

Sam ate ____ sweet.

Help ____ to lift this.

____ can help you.

NOW TRY THIS!

- **Write a note asking someone to tea using these:**

I   me   my

Teachers' note Remind the children about *I* as a word to use instead of their name and that this is always a capital letter. Ask them what other word they can use for themselves (*me*) and invite them to give some sentences containing *I* or *me*. Ask them to say a sentence containing *my* and discuss how it is different from *I* and *me*. Draw out that it is used for things that belong to them.

Instead of names

You use I instead of your name.

What can you use instead of these names?

- **Draw lines to join each picture to a word.**

he | it | she | they

- **Write** he, she, it **or** they **instead of the word in the box.**

Dad ______________ gave me a pound.

I saw a bird. The bird ______________ was a robin.

Mum ______________ is at work.

Ella and Raj ______________ have gone to Spain.

NOW TRY THIS!

- **Write four other sentences beginning with these:** He | It | She | They
- **Rewrite them with names of people or things in the boxes.**

Teachers' note Review the children's previous learning about words to use instead of their name. Ask them if they would use *he* or *she* for the child sitting next to them. How do they know which to use? Ask if they would use one of these words for a lot of people. Introduce *them*. Hold up an object such as a pencil and ask if they would use *he, she, they,* or another word for *it*. Introduce *it*.

Belonging words

• **Link everyone to the** belonging **words.**

me

you

Dad

Mum

a bird

us

Mum and Dad

Mrs Shine

Mr Trip

me

Ella and Sita

us

me

a hamster

its

their

her

my

his

your

our

NOW TRY THIS!

• **Write sentences using these words.**

my | your | his | her | its | our | their

chers' note Review the children's previous learning about *my* as a word for things that belong them. Which word would they use for something belonging to the child sitting next to them? cuss why different answers are correct from different children. Which word would they use to lace *the dog's* in *the dog's kennel*, or *Jack and Jill* in *Jack and Jill's bucket*?

Where words

There are a lot of words for where. Here are some of them

Where word-bank

across	along	by	down	in	near
next to	on	over	under	up	

- **Write where words in the gaps.**

1 Alex hid ________________ the duvet.

2 Sunita fell ________________ the stairs.

3 When it was safe we walked ________________ the road.

4 There was no one ________________ the house.

5 We had to go ________________ a steep hill.

6 There was a car park ________________ the shops.

7 He sang as he walked ________________ the road.

8 Roop's house is ________________ mine.

9 There were two mugs ________________ the table.

10 The school is ________________ a park.

NOW TRY THIS!

- **Write three sentences about a walk.**
- **Use as many where words as you can.**

Teachers' note Review the children's previous learning about the different parts of a sentence by reminding them of the questions they were asked: *Who? What? When? Where*? Read the words in the word-bank and draw out that they can be used in sentences to say where something happened.

Tell me when

- **Read what they say.**
- **Fill in the gaps.**
- **Then write the sentences.**

Yesterday.

Geeta was here

I went to Florida.

Last year.

I went

We met the Queen.

On Friday.

There was a storm.

At 2 o'clock.

– when you were five
– when you last went swimming
– when the weather was cold

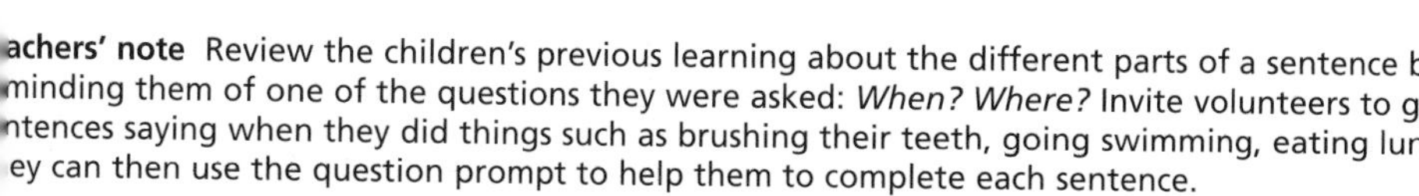
achers' note Review the children's previous learning about the different parts of a sentence by minding them of one of the questions they were asked: *When? Where?* Invite volunteers to give ntences saying when they did things such as brushing their teeth, going swimming, eating lunch. ey can then use the question prompt to help them to complete each sentence.

It's like this

What are they like?

- **Join each picture to a word.**
- **Write a sentence about it.**

cold
hot
sour
soft
sweet
rough
salty

The cat feels ______________________________.

A lemon is ______________________________.

The lollipop tastes ______________________________.

The kettle is ______________________________.

Stones are ______________________________.

Snow is ______________________________.

Crisps are ______________________________.

NOW TRY THIS!

- **Write two sentences about how other things feel.**

Teachers' note Explain that some sentences tell readers what something is like. Invite volunteers to say what each item in the pictures is like and to find the word it should be linked to. They can draw lines to join the objects to the descriptions and then write sentences about them.

Words for doing

- **Circle ten words for** doing **.**
- **Write one of them in each gap.**

g	r	o	w	s	o	n	i	r	e	a	d
y	z	w	a	s	h	o	h	d	p	i	r
b	c	r	o	q	o	s	k	a	t	e	i
p	n	i	a	r	p	w	n	d	o	w	n
c	a	t	k	n	d	i	i	u	a	s	k
q	l	e	j	x	c	m	t	o	p	e	o

1 The sun and rain make plants ____________ .

2 We ____________ comics and books.

3 I ____________ water and orange juice.

4 Ella can ____________ neatly.

5 Sam can ____________ a long way.

6 Sometimes I ____________ on one leg.

7 In the morning I ____________ my face.

8 We like to ____________ on the frozen pond.

- **Write sentences with the other two** doing **words.**

achers' note Remind the children that a sentence always contains a word to say what someone something *does*. Ask for examples. The children can then look through the word search for ords for *doing*. Point out that these can read across or down the page. Once they have found the ords they can use eight of them in the sentences below the word search.

Question words

- **Write** question **words in the gaps.**

Question word-bank

How	Where
What	Which
When	Who
	Why

________ has been eating my porridge?

________ do we have to climb this hill?

________ are little boys made of?

________ is the boy who looks after the sheep?

________ can we find our way home?

________ will a prince come and get me out of here?

________ little pig shall I eat?

NOW TRY THIS!

- **Write three questions for story characters to ask.**
- **Start with a** question **word.**

Teachers' note Review the children's previous learning about the different parts of a sentence. Discuss how they can tell that the sentences on this page are questions. (Point out the question marks.) Model how to complete the first example by trying different words in the gap and saying, 'No, that's not right' until the correct on is found. Read the question and say, 'Yes, that's right.'

Special names

Circle the words which need a capital letter.

Write the words on the notepad.

Remember the capital letters.

Little polly flinders sat among the cinders.

lucy locket lost her pocket. kitty fisher found it.

monday 1 april

solomon grundy was born on a monday.

Little jack horner sat in a corner, eating his christmas pie.

The grand old duke of york had ten thousand men.....

NOW TRY THIS!

- **Write sentences about these.**

a king who was a merry old soul	a bridge which is falling down

Think about the nursery rhymes.

achers' note Review the children's previous learning about capital letters for names of people ıd places. Tell them that there are other special names which have capital letters: festivals, onths and days. Invite volunteers to come out and write up an example of each.

Addresses

The names of these start with a capital letter.

buildings	streets	villages, towns and cities	countries

- **Write the names and addresses on the envelopes.**

Remember the capital letters.

My name is james dunn.
I live at hollybush farm.
It is in burn lane and my
village is sheepcross.

My name is
wayne morton. I live at
number 324 harbour street in
a suburb called bondi. This is
in sydney in australia.

- **Write your full name and address.**
- **Write a friend's name and address.**
- **Write the postcodes.**

Teachers' note Review the children's previous learning about capital letters for names of people, places, festivals, months and days. Ask volunteers to name their house or street and invite them to come out and write it. What is special about the first letter? Help volunteers to write up their address, line by line. Point out that each word begins with a capital letter.

Book titles

'he main words in book titles each have a capital letter.

Write the titles of these books.

Word-bank & name-bank

beanstalk
billy
boots
dwarfs
gingerbread
goats
gruff
hood
jack
little
man
puss
red
riding
seven
snow
three
white

NOW TRY THIS!

- **Write the titles of three other books.**

'achers' note Hold up some books. What do children notice about the way the titles are written? 'me might be written completely in capital letters, a few might be all lower-case but most use capital 'tters for the main words. Look for examples of words which are not main words: for example, *a, the, 'd, its, their*. If necessary, check that the children recognise the book covers on this page.

Flying sentences

- **Write the sentences.**
- **Put in the capital letters and full stops.**

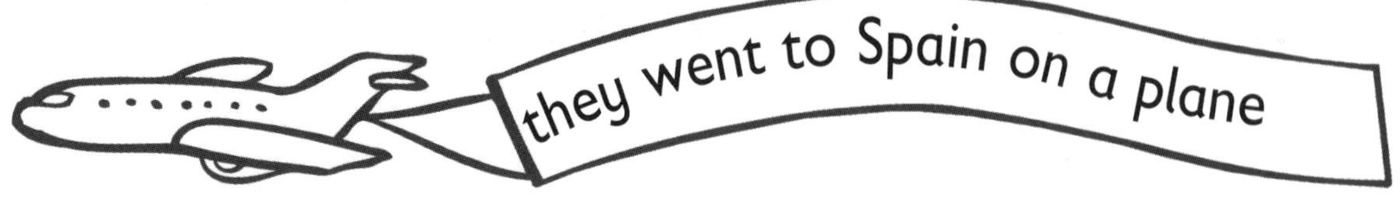
they went to Spain on a plane

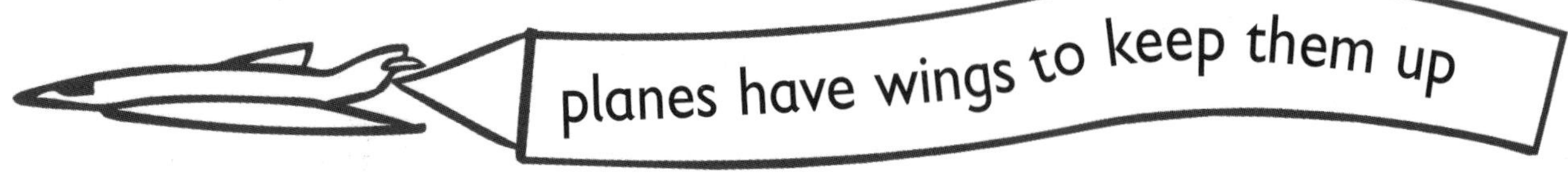
planes have wings to keep them up

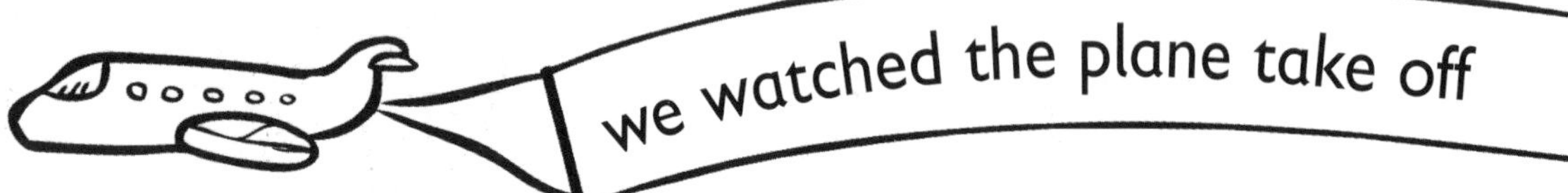
we watched the plane take off

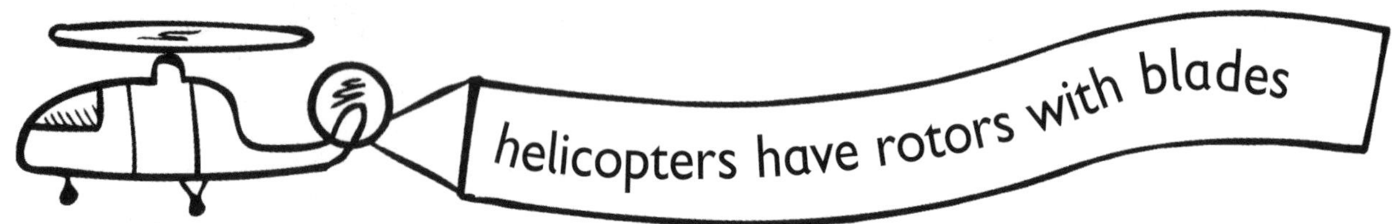
helicopters have rotors with blades

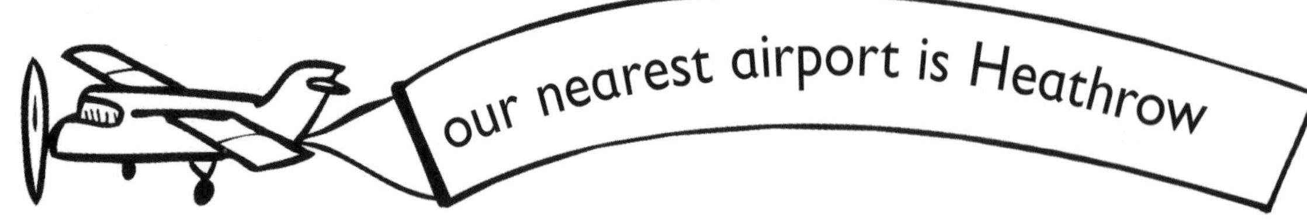
our nearest airport is Heathrow

NOW TRY THIS!

- **Write these sentences with capital letters and full stops.**

planes have flaps on their wings these are called ailerons they can make the plane go up or down

Teachers' note Review the children's previous learning about starting sentences with capital letters and ending them with full stops. They can then copy and correct the sentences on the banners.

Question mark

This is a question mark.
It goes at the end of a question.

- **Read the sentences. Are they questions? ✓ or ✗**

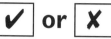

This is a lion. ☐

Where is my teddy? ☐

Where are you going? ☐

What time is it? ☐

I like ice cream. ☐

It is six o'clock. ☐

- **Circle the question marks.**

- **Write three questions.**
- **Put question marks at the end of them.**

eachers' note Remind the children of their work on full stops. Tell them that some sentences ask a uestion and that these end with a question mark. They could practise drawing full stops at the ight size and on the line on which they write. They can then read the sentences and decide vhether they ask a question.

Question queen

- **Show the question queen where to put question marks.**
- **Show her where to put full stops.**

When can we go to the beach

Why is the sky blue

We can go there today

I like to play tennis

What shall we do

Where is the ball

Shall we play ball

Who is that boy

It is in the box

It's too cold to go to the beach

- **Write two questions.**
- **Write the answers.**

Remember . and ?.

Teachers' note The children should first have completed page 45. Ask them if the first sentence is a question. What does it ask? Ask them where the sentence ends and if they should put a full stop or a question mark at the end of it. They can then read the other sentences and decide whether they should end with a question mark or a full stop.

Email check

Put in the full stops and questions marks.

To | Cc | Subject

Lara :-)

Thanks for your email. I'm much better now I'm going back to school tomorrow Are your brothers back yet

How did you get on in the swimming gala I hope you had a good time I'm going to a swimming club next week I've got a new swimsuit

It's half term next week We're going to Wales Nan and Grandad are coming too We've booked a cottage by the sea Have you been to Wales

Can you come to our house when we get back Ask your mum

Love Annie x

NOW TRY THIS!

- **Write a short reply from Lara to Annie.**
- **Put some questions in it.**

achers' note Review the children's understanding of full stops and question marks. Tell them that ey are going to read an email which someone sent without reading it through to check it. plain that the full stops and question marks are missing and that their task is to put them in. mind them that a sentence is not the same as a line of writing.

Question time

You can turn a sentence **into a** question **.**

Sentence It is raining today.

Question Is it raining today?

- **Turn these sentences into questions.**

1 This is Ali's bike.

2 May can skip fast.

3 He has a new phone.

4 His dogs are corgis.

5 We can go to the party.

6 She will win the race.

1 ______________________________

2 ______________________________

3 ______________________________

4 ______________________________

5 ______________________________

6 ______________________________

- **Turn these sentences into questions.**

He knows the answer.

They are playing chess.

Teachers' note How can you tell if a question is a sentence, even if there is no question mark? Draw out that they can start with a question word or words can be turned around: *it is/is it, she has/has she*. Write up a sentence for the children to make into a question by changing the positions of two words: for example, *He is going home*. Remind them to change the full stop to a question mark.

The comma

This is a comma ,.

You can put a comma after each part of a list.

In my pocket I have
a conker, a sweet, a mouse
and some sawdust.

You don't need a comma before and.

- **Put the commas in the sentences.**

1 At the party I saw Leo Tom Bella and Sunita.

2 Each wizard had a wand an owl a cat and a broomstick.

3 We played football cricket rounders and tennis.

4 The playground had a slide swings a roundabout a seesaw and a climbing frame.

5 Along the road we found a beech tree two oaks a lime and a rowan.

6 My gran gave me a pound some felt-tips a pen and a ruler.

Remember – no comma before and.

NOW TRY THIS!

- **Write a sentence to list your favourite toys.**
- **Put a comma after each part of the list.**

Teachers' note Show examples of vertically listed items, such as shopping lists. Draw out that they are not written as sentences. Explain that a list can be part of a sentence. Read the first example and draw out how the commas are used to separate the items. Write up the same sentence without commas and read it aloud. Emphasise the way in which the words run into one another without a pause.

What do you know?

These questions ask for information.
- **Write sentences to answer them.**

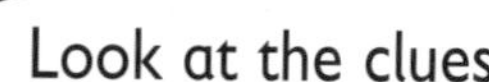

What do we call a baby cow?

We call a

What is the date of Halloween?

What is the word for a very small river?

Which parts of a plant are under the ground?

- **Write a question you want to answer.**
- **Write a sentence to answer it.**

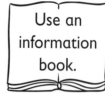

Use an information book.

Teachers' note Discuss the purpose of questions – to find something out. Draw out that questions are asked in order to get an answer. Tell them that they will find the answers to these questions in the clues on the page and that they should write the answers as sentences. Remind them about the capital letter and full stop.

Instruction search

• **Which sentences are instructions? ✔ or ✗**

Keep off the grass.

Shall we play cards?

There will be a sale at 4 o'clock.

First you give each player seven cards.

Please drive slowly.

I am having a party on Saturday at 6 o'clock.

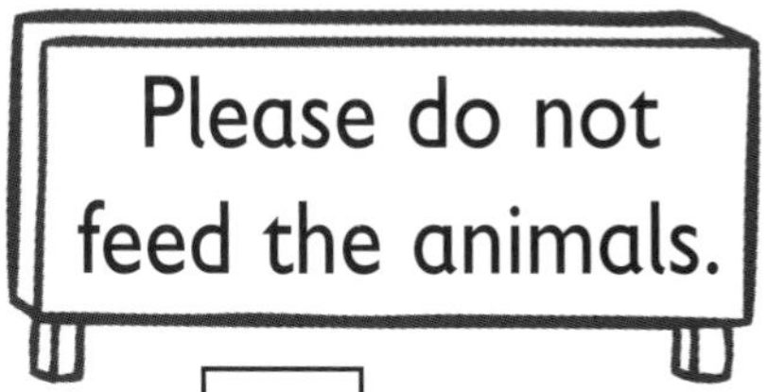

Please do not feed the animals.

First I mixed the flour and butter.

Please take a leaflet.

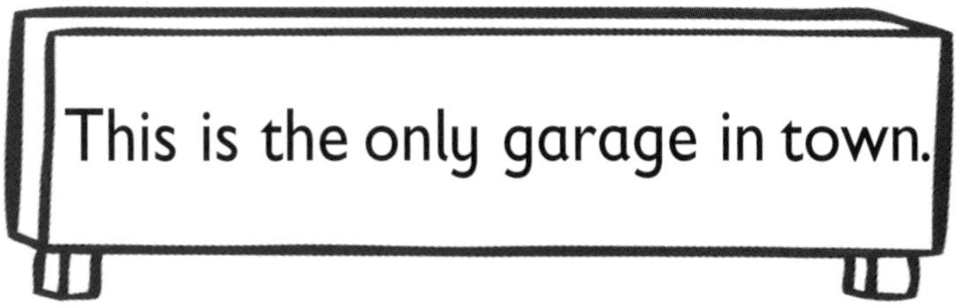

This is the only garage in town.

NOW TRY THIS!

• **Make up two instructions for children at your school.**

Teachers' note Review the different types of sentence and their purposes: telling a story, asking a question, giving information. Introduce the instruction sentence, which tells the reader what to do. Read the first example with the children and ask if it is an instruction. Draw out that it is because it tells people what to do. Ask the children how it is different from an information sentence.

Recipe sentences

- **Find the sentence for each picture. Write it in the box.**

Shortbread

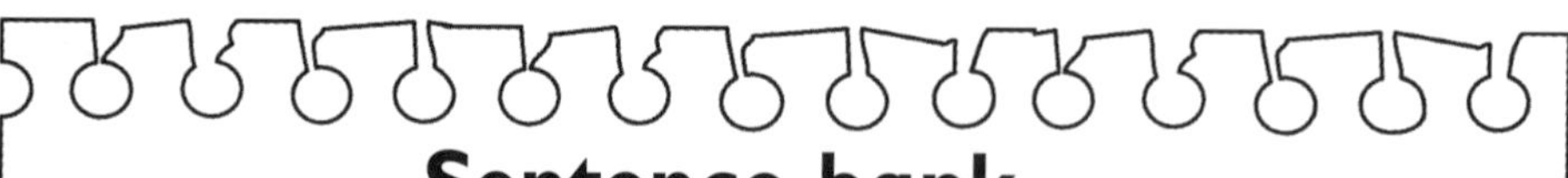

Sentence-bank

Bake it in a hot oven for 20 minutes.

Rub in the flour, sugar and butter.

Flatten the mixture into a baking tray.

Roll the mixture into a ball.

What should you do before you begin baking?

- **Write an instruction sentence.**

Teachers' note Show the children examples of recipes and discuss the type of sentence they use (instruction – telling the reader what to do). Ask them what the first picture tells them to do and help them to express this as a sentence. Remind them about the capital letter, commas and full stop.

Note it

- **Look at the picture of Tern Island. What can you find out about the island?**
- **Write notes.**

Notes do not need to be in sentences.

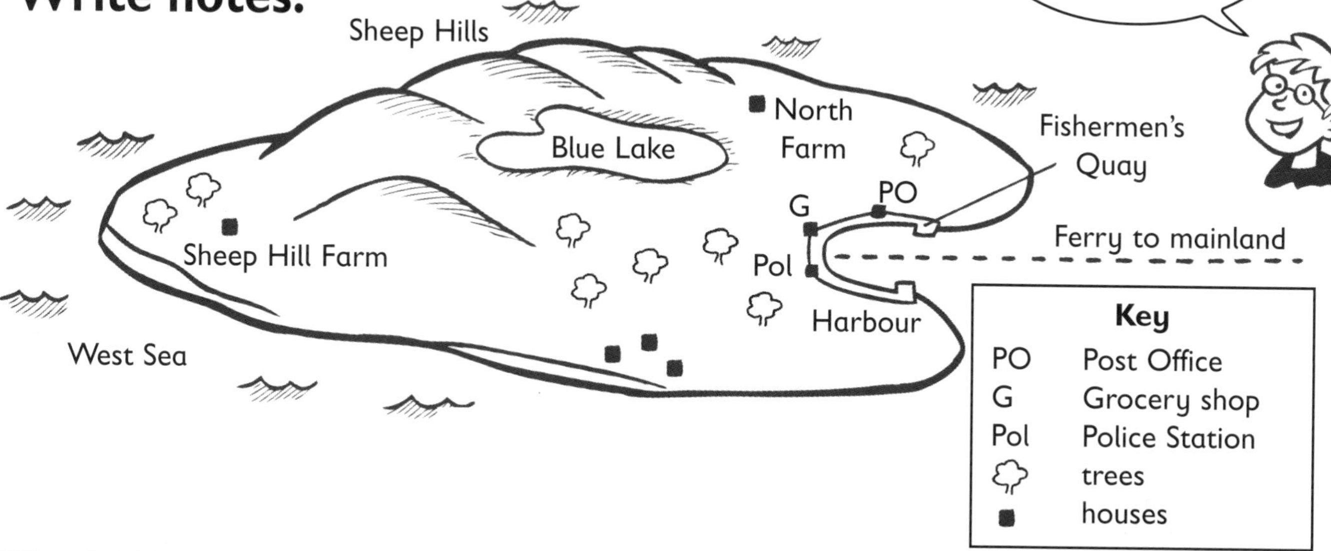

Notes

Sea all around

Post office

NOW TRY THIS!

- **Swap notes with a partner.**
- **Write sentences from the notes.**

achers' note Explain that when we are finding out information to answer questions it is quicker write notes which are not sentences. Show them the example (*Sea all around*) and discuss the ords which have been missed out and which could make it into a sentence: <u>There is</u> *sea all around* <u>island</u>.

Notes to sentences

Gemma has written notes about the seaside.

- **Help her to write sentences.**

Notes	Sentences
Flat sandy beach	The beach is
Sand dunes along beach	
Grass on sand dunes	
No rocks	
No buildings	
Hardly any people	
A lot of sea birds	
Seaweed on sand	

NOW TRY THIS!

- **Write three sentences from notes you have written.**

Teachers' note The children should first have completed page 53. Remind them of how they wrote notes – writing only the important words. Point out that these can later be turned into sentences and remind them how *Sea all around* was turned into a sentence. Ask them to read the notes and decide what information each note gives. Help them to express the first example as a sentence.

Island key

- Read the key.

Write sentences about the islands.

Key			
	bridge to mainland		people live there
	road across beach		grocery shop
	ferry		post office
	no traffic		school

Holy Island

Sark

Ulva

NOW TRY THIS!

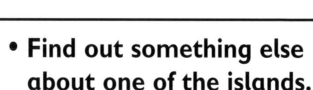

- **Find out something else about one of the islands.**
- **Write a sentence about it.**

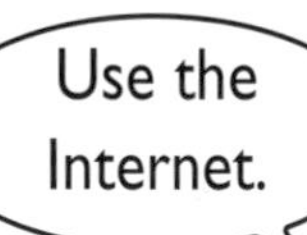

eachers' note Discuss where the children have seen keys which explain how symbols are used for iving information. Look for examples in the local environment: road signs, shop signs, notices, oad markings and so on (also washing instructions inside clothing). Draw out that symbols have to e used carefully so that people know what they mean and that sometimes a key is needed.

Reading a chart

- **Look at the weather chart.**
- **Write a long sentence about the weather each day.**

Monday	Tuesday	Wednesday	Thursday	Friday

Key

sun

cloud

rain

wind

sun and showers

On Monday ______________________________

On ______________________________

____

____

____

NOW TRY THIS!

- **Record today's weather at different times.**
- **Use symbols.**
- **Write sentences about it.**

Teachers' note The children might be familiar with these or other, similar, weather symbols. Discuss why symbols are useful. Draw out that they can give information much more quickly than writing – as long as the readers know what they mean. Draw out that a key is sometimes necessary. Ask the children to use the chart to find out about each day's weather and to write a sentence about it.

Chart it

- **Read the report.**
- **Fill in the chart.**
- **Tick the places where the animals were found.** ✓

Animals in the school grounds

Emily found a spider on the truck of a tree and Jason found one on a wall. There was a snail on the wall, too. We looked under a stone and saw some woodlice and there were woodlice on a tree trunk. In the soil we found some worms. There were ladybirds on the flowers, leaves and stems of some plants and a bee on a flower.

	flower	leaf	soil	stem	under stone	tree trunk	wall
bee							
ladybird							
snail							
spider							
woodlouse							
worm							

- **Make a chart about animals around your school.**

Teachers' note Explain that sometimes information is easier to record on a chart than in writing and that it can be much easier to read a chart than a long piece of writing. The children should read the information and then record it on the chart. Begin with the bee. Ask where it was seen and show the children how to record this under the correct heading on the chart.

It's magnetic

- **Look at the diagram.**
- **Read the labels.**
- **Write sentences about the magnet.**

A horseshoe magnet

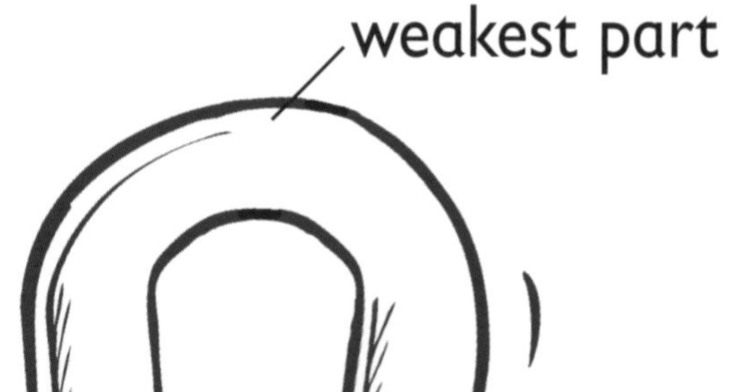

1 The picture shows a ______________________

2 It picks up ______________________

3 It doesn't ______________________

4 The strongest ______________________

5 They are ______________________

6 The weakest ______________________

- **Find out something else about a horseshoe magnet.**
- **Write notes on the diagram.**
- **Write a sentence about it.**

Teachers' note With the children, read the caption and ask them what the diagram shows. What do the labels tell them about the horseshoe magnet? Ask volunteers to read a label aloud and ask if this is a sentence. Can they make it into a sentence? They should complete the text below the diagram in the form of sentences.

Patterns in poems

Read these parts of poems.
Are they sentences? 

Up and down
Up and down
All the way to London Town. ☐

Mrs Brown went to town,
Riding on a pony. ☐

Rain, rain, go away.
Come again another day. ☐

Jelly on the plate,
Jelly on the plate. ☐

Wibble, wobble,
Wibble, wobble,
Jelly on the plate. ☐

Five little owls in an old elm tree,
Fluffy and puffy as owls could be. ☐

I eat my peas with honey. ☐

I've done it all my life. ☐

It makes the peas taste funny,
But it keeps them on the knife. ☐

- **Copy another poem.**
- **Underline the sentences in different colours.**

eachers' note Read the first example and ask the children how they can tell that this is from a oem and not another type of text. Ask them if it is a sentence, and how they can tell. Draw ttention to the repeated language. Discuss the next example. Point out the rhyming words. Repeat or the other examples and help the children say how they can recognise that they are poems.

Fun change

- **Change a word in each sentence to make it funny.**
- **Circle one word to change.**
- **Write the new word in the box.**

Mrs Kirk walked to work.

Mr Parr washed the car.

Brian Moore washed the floor.

Farmer Day cut the hay.

Mr Most lives by the coast.

NOW TRY THIS!

- **Write three funny rhyming sentences.**

Teachers' note Ask the volunteers to read the examples and ask if each one is a sentence. How can we tell? Discuss how the first one can be made funny by changing one word: for example, *walked* could be changed to *swam, rolled* or *hopped*.

That's a laugh

- **This sentence is nonsense:**

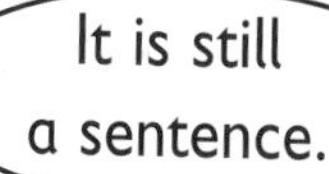

I saw a snail with a broken leg chase a fish across a field.

- **Write your own nonsense sentences.**

saw a cat with ______________________________

ush ____________________ up the ____________________.

saw a ____________________ with a basket of shopping

______________________________.

saw a ____________________ with a mobile phone

______________________________.

saw an elephant with ____________________ fly

ith a ____________________ across the ____________________.

saw ______________________________.

NOW TRY THIS!

- **Write two nonsense sentences which begin like this:**

In our street there lives ____________________.

chers' note Remind the children of their previous learning about sentences and how we can tell set of words is a sentence. Remind them that a sentence can be silly but it is still a sentence. ore they begin this page they could practise playing with words to make up silly sentences with end.

Loud words

Words in [*italics*] are stressed.

- **Read this to a friend:**

  "No," she said. "I was at *home*, not in *Rome*."

- **Read these with a friend.**
- **Circle the *stressed* words.**

We have no apples but you can have a *banana*.

This can't be a *zoo*. There are no animals.

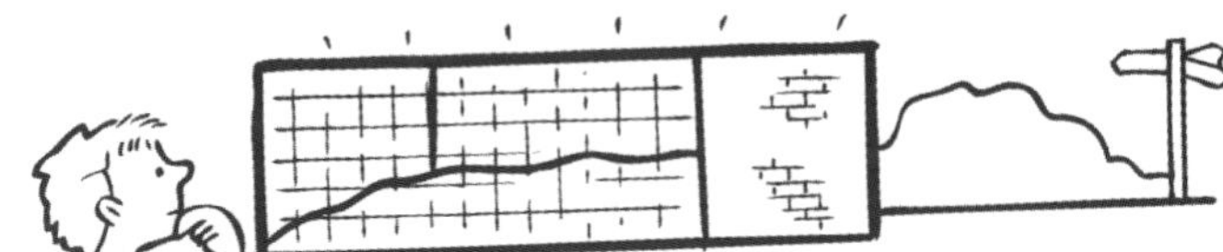

I've been waiting for *two hours*.

I can't tell you, because it's a *secret*.

That's not my coat – it's *his*.

We can't walk there – it's too *far*.

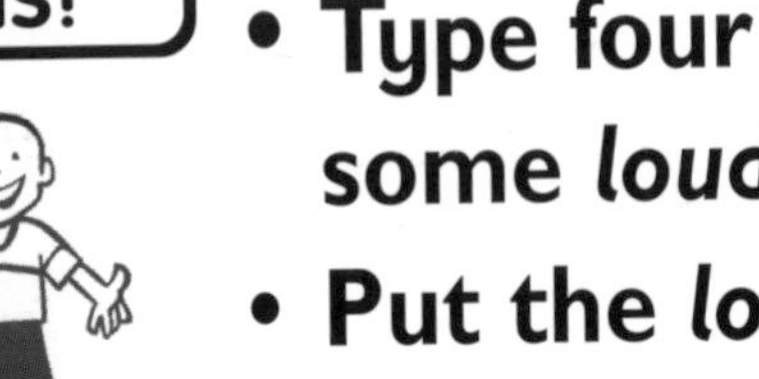

- **Type four sentences with some *loud* words.**
- **Put the *loud* words in *italics*.**

Teachers' note Show the children examples of fiction or poetry in which some words are printed in italics to ensure that they understand the term *italic*. They could also practise changing text into italics on the computer. Discuss why italics are used and draw out that it is to stress a word or set of words. The children should read the sentences aloud, stressing the italicised words.

LOUD words

Words in CAPITAL LETTERS are said a little louder than others.

rang the bell and a GORILLA came to the door!

Circle the (loud) **words.**

Copy the sentences.

Write the (loud) **words in capital letters.**

I asked for toast – not a ghost.

____

____

____

Stop," shouted the girl, s the robber ook her bag.

____

____

____

heir teacher was dressed as Dracula.

____

____

____

NOW TRY THIS!

- **Act a story with a friend.**
- **Write what you said.**

Use CAPITAL LETTERS for loud words.

hers' note Begin by showing examples of fiction or poetry in which some words are printed in tal letters. Discuss why capitals are used and draw out that it is to stress a word or set of words. tals are more often used in speech and indicate words the speaker emphasises or even shouts. children should read the sentences aloud, stressing the words in capitals.

That's silly

This is silly, but it is still a sentence:

She went for a swim in the custard.

This is not silly, but it is not a sentence:

Two old men on a bench in the park.

- **Join these to make silly sentences.**

I saw a frog	in case the comb's teeth bite him.
Two old octopuses	and brushed her teeth.
Alex won't comb his hair	goes to town in a space ship.
Tina sat at the piano	were singing a merry song.
The sea bed	is where whales sleep.
My gran	driving a bus.

NOW TRY THIS!

- **Write four silly sentences starting like this.**

A can of beans | A sausage
Two rockets | The King lost his socks

Teachers' note Remind the children of their previous work on silly sentences and provide examples of silly sentences from poems or jokes for them to read aloud. Help them to pair the first example with the end of a sentence to make something silly or funny. They should draw a line to link them and then read the sentence with a friend.